Praise for "Eddie's Tale"

"What an amazing book... I'm extremely impressed...
EDDIE'S TALE is like Dr. Seuss meets Dr. Joslin. I was never able to explain my diabetes to my six-year-old daughter in a way she could fully understand. Now she finally gets it!"
Gary Scheiner, MS, CDE. Author, "Think Like a Pancreas"
Owner and Clinical Director, Integrated Diabetes Services

"Cleverly and sensitively written, in a style that makes it easy for a youngster to grasp the complexities of his or her condition,
EDDIE'S TALE is a must-read for any family that has a young child with type 1 diabetes."
Bruce Buckingham, M.D. Professor, Pediatrics
Division of Endocrinology and Diabetes, Stanford University

"I love [this] book – it's a perfect introduction to type 1 diabetes for young kids, as well as for their siblings, friends and classmates."
Jeff Hitchcock, Creator, Editor and Webmaster, Children With Diabetes

"**EDDIE'S TALE** is a terrific way for children (and adults) to gain greater insight into one of the most common chronic childhood conditions and one that has few outward signs. The well-drawn illustrations and clear story make it easy for people to bridge the knowledge gap on type 1 diabetes, an illness that affects millions of Americans."
Mark Fischer-Colbrie, Parent of a type 1 diabetic,
Ten-Year Volunteer, Juvenile Diabetes Research Foundation

"The illustrations are delightful and engaging; sure to help many toddlers with diabetes."
Theresa Garnero, APRN, BC-ADM, MSN, CDE
Author/Illustrator, "Your First Year With Diabetes"

EDDIE'S TALE

A Young Child's Introduction to Type 1 Diabetes

Written and Illustrated by Sue Kowalski

EDDIE'S TALE

A Young Child's Introduction to Type 1 Diabetes

Written and Illustrated by Sue Kowalski

ISBN 978-1-935530-35-0

First Edition January 2011

Published by Park Place Publications

Pacific Grove, CA 93950

www.ParkPlacePublications.com

For Hayden

And his loving big sister

Emily Grace

Eddie the kitten did not want to play.
He said to his mom, "I don't feel well today!
I'm tired and thirsty, and sure need to pee ---
Gosh, what in the world is the matter with me?!"

His mama decided right then and right there,
to visit Doc Whiskers, for medical care.

"Oh, Doctor," moaned Eddie, "I need something to drink!
I'm sleepy, and may have to pee more, I think!
I just don't know why I am feeling so crummy ---
I'm dizzy, and I'm getting sick to my tummy!"

The doctor said, "I'll run a health test or two.
We'll soon see what's happening inside of you."

Then, lo and behold, soon the answer was clear:
Diabetes had come! Diabetes was here!

Doc Whiskers said, "Eddie, now don't be afraid -
But inside your body a war has been made.
Inside your body two armies did fight ---
Each army thought that its own side was right!

"Your **insulin army** worked really hard,
giving you energy to play in your yard.
The other big army wants you to stay well;
it **keeps out bad germs** that around you may dwell.

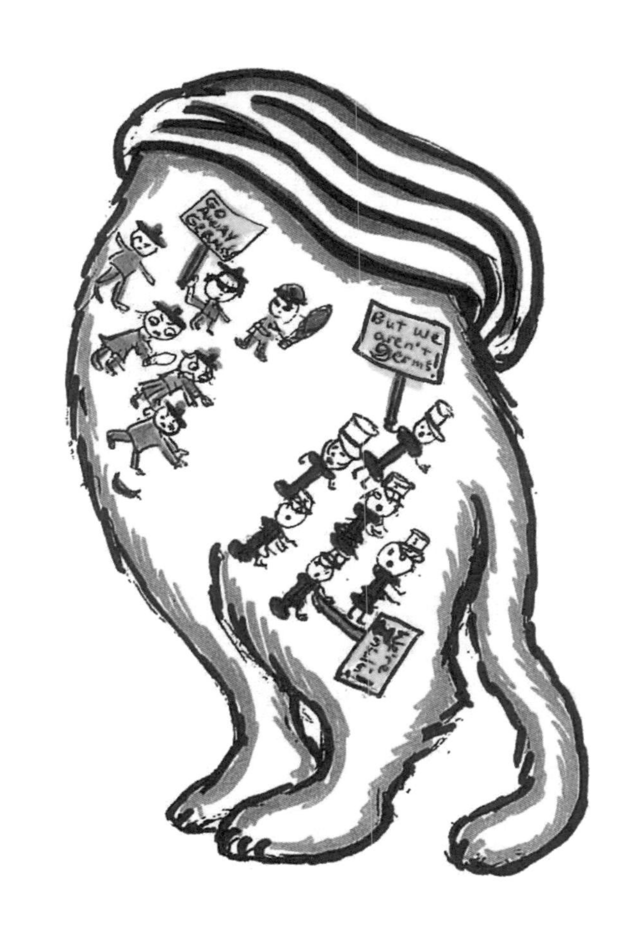

"But the **germ-fighting army** had a very wrong thought:
'This **insulin army** needs to be fought!'
Then it chased out your **insulin army** – too bad!
It just got mixed-up --- now, please don't be mad.

"So your body needs **insulin** some other way.
A pump or some shots will indeed save the day."

"But Doc," cried young Eddie, "why'd this happen to ME?
Did I mess up my room, or watch too much TV?
And how come it's ME who'll get poked and get stuck??
How come it's ME who has all this bad luck??"

"Diabetes is sneaky," Doc Whiskers replied.
"It picks some, not others, in which to go hide.
And nobody's certain just why this is so.
But you can be happy and healthy --- I know!

"Why, you'll still be able to drink and to eat
all your favorite things, even ones that are sweet.
You don't need to worry: you'll be fine and do great ---
Once more you'll be able to climb and to skate!

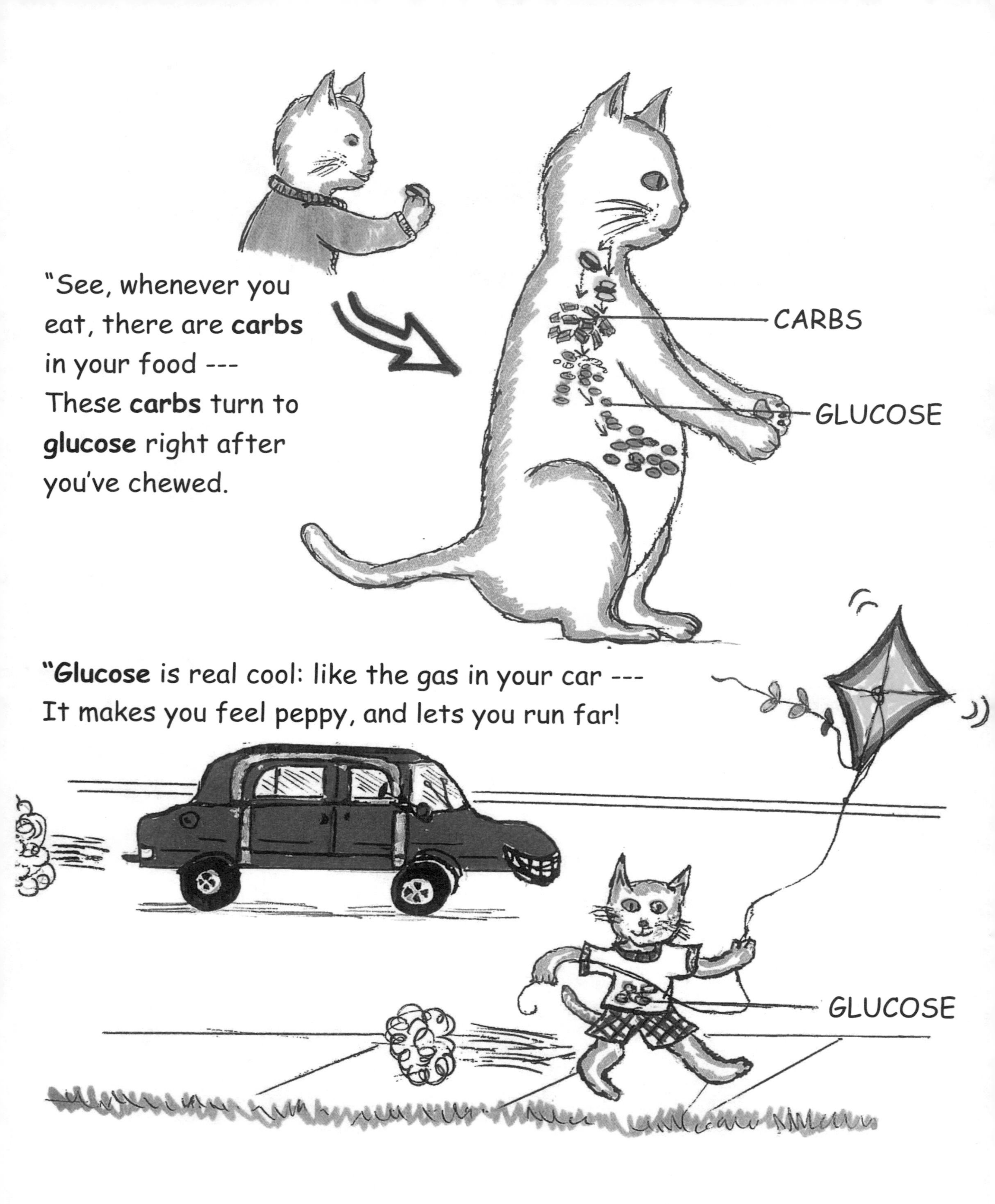
"See, whenever you eat, there are **carbs** in your food ---
These **carbs** turn to **glucose** right after you've chewed.
CARBS
GLUCOSE
"**Glucose** is real cool: like the gas in your car ---
It makes you feel peppy, and lets you run far!
GLUCOSE

"Now, remember your **insulin army**, so brave?
Its job was to make your **glucose** behave.
But because it's not there, because it lost the war,
It's just not around, to help any more!
So without enough **insulin** to make it stay right,
your **glucose** can fall low, or climb high, out of sight ---

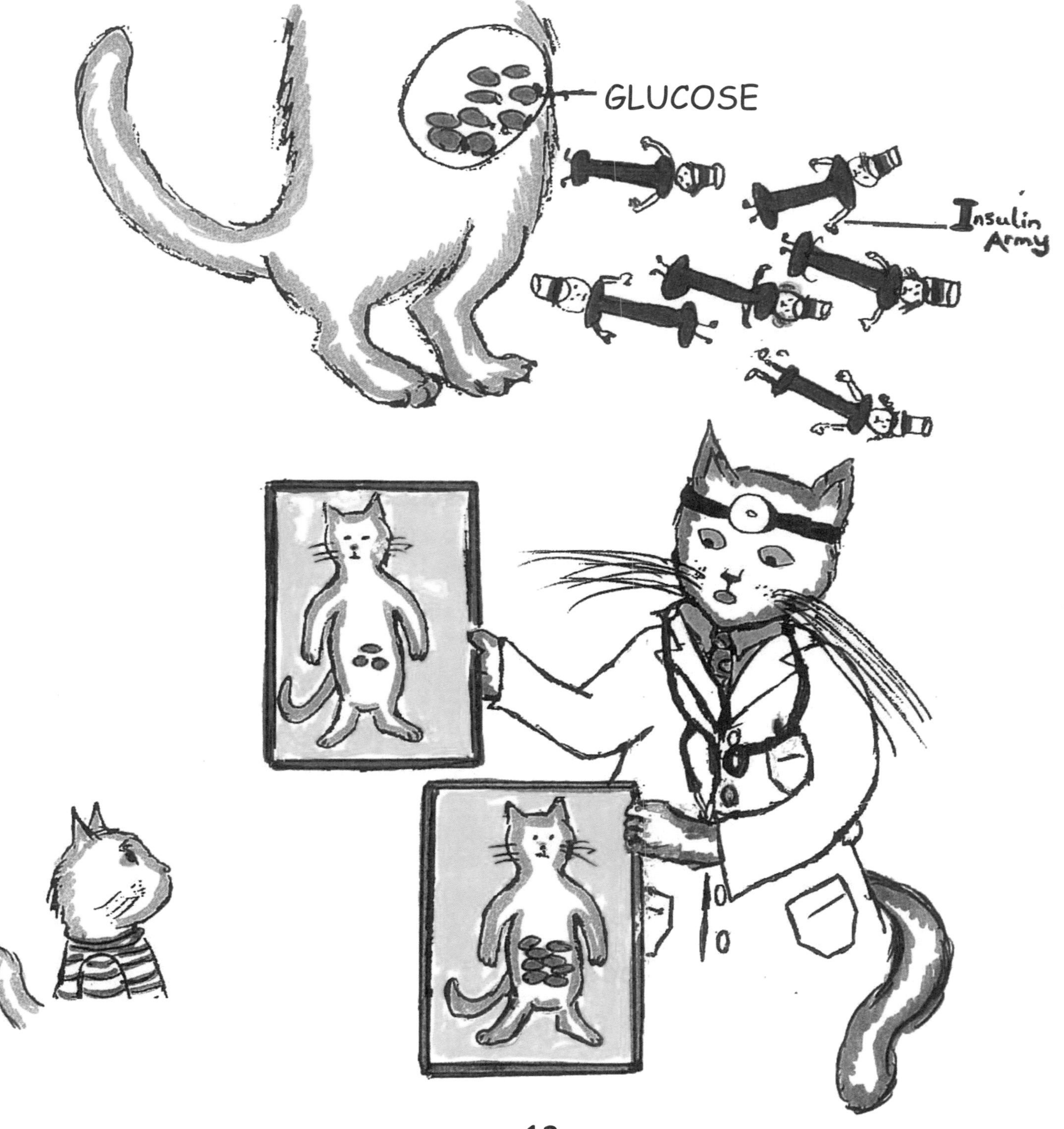

"And the funny thing is,
sometimes you won't know
if it's leaped up real high,
or has dropped very low.

"You may just feel cranky or crabby, or gruff

"or simply confused, like your head's full of fluff.

"Now comes the time for a blood check to know
which way that your **glucose** is starting to go!

"If it's low, you'll feel wobbly, or may want to sleep,
or be hungry, meowing for food in a **HEAP**.
When you think that your glucose is starting to fall
be sure to give someone **A VERY LOUD CALL**!"

"But, Doc," Eddie asked, "If my **glucose** gets **HIGH??**
will it climb up real far --- all the way to the sky??"

"No way," said Doc Whiskers, "but you'll want lots to drink,
and you'll pee like a river, and then you will think ---
'It's time for some **insulin**, through a pump or a shot!
To make sure my **glucose** comes down a whole lot!'

"Diabetes is a see-saw, to try and keep steady:
Too low or too high is not good for you, Eddie!

"So eat the right foods --- Mom and Dad will choose what ---
Please listen to them: they both know a lot.

"Then to deal with your **glucose** in just the right way,
they'll be checking your blood both by night and by day
to make sure your **glucose** is at a good place,
and to keep a big happy smile on your face!"

Eddie the kitten, he thought for a bit ---
Then he leaped up, and his eyes were both lit.
"So I'll do what you say --- I can still really shine:
I'll listen to Mom and to Dad, and be fine.

"I'll have my blood checked, by day and by night,
and I'll take my **insulin**, and try to eat right.

"OK, Guys," he shouted, "I think that I see:
Diabetes will not get the better of me!"

Doc Whiskers purred loudly, and Mama did, too.
They both cried, "Oh, Eddie, we're so proud of you!"

Then Doc said, "I'll give you some **insulin** now,
so you'll soon feel better --- and then to learn how
to stay very healthy and keep yourself fit,
you'll need to start visiting me quite a bit!

"So Bye for now, but before you and Mom leave,
look right over here: I have tricks up my sleeve ---
You'll need these at home, so take them away,
and I'll see you real soon, on some other day!"

Late that night, safe and snug in his bed,
Eddie thought over what Doc Whiskers said.
"'Eat well and get blood checks; take **insulin**, too' ---
Why, this won't be hard, although some of it's new.
I'll do what is right, or my name isn't Eddie!
OK, Diabetes, bring it on! I am **READY!!!**"

ACKNOWLEDGEMENTS

"Eddie Tale" could not have been told
without the invaluable help of the following individuals,
in alphabetical order:

Janet Fire
Laurie Gibson
Patricia Hamilton
Kellie Kowalski
Mike Kowalski
Nancy Lunetta
Ellen Maserati
Annie Moyer
Laszlo Papp
Kathleen Virmani
Janet Wade
Amy Walker

Photo: William Frank

Sue Kowalski is an
attorney, artist, founder of
an international adoption agency,
travel consultant, and grandma to
Hayden, diagnosed with type 1 diabetes
at age two, and now five. Sue and her husband
live in Northern California.

About "Eddie's Tale"

The idea of Eddie the kitten with type 1 diabetes came to me one evening in 2010 during a visit to my Missouri grandchildren, eight-year-old Emily Grace and Hayden, who had just turned five. Hayden has lived with T1D since he was twenty-seven months old. He wears an insulin pump as well as a continuous glucose monitoring system. As he dawdled over his dessert, I was aware that his mother had to urge him to finish in order to keep his numbers in balance. My son was nearby, and when I asked him whether he thought that Hayden had understood why he had to eat all his ice cream, he replied, "More or less."

"'More or less' is just not good enough," I told myself. "Someone needs to write a book to show these little ones just what is going on inside their bodies and why they need to eat right, take insulin, and be checked regularly." When I returned home to California, I realized that I could, and should, answer this need. I hope that "Eddie's Tale" will make the basic concepts of type 1 diabetes easy enough for small children to understand.

I am currently working on a sequel, following Eddie the kitten as he goes to school and is better able to comprehend his diabetes. My love and best wishes go out to all the children, parents and physicians as they make their way in the world of type 1 diabetes.

Sue Kowalski